LAST ORDERS

The Essential Guide to Your
Letter of Wishes

Patricia C. Byron

Published in 2010 by:
Stellar Books
Dunham Gatehouse
Charcoal Road
Bowdon
Cheshire
WA14 4RY

www.stellarbooks.co.uk
www.lastorders.org

© Patricia C Byron 2010

Patricia C Byron asserts the moral rights to be identified as the author of this work.

ISBN 9780956508904

A catalogue record for this book is available at the British Library

All rights reserved. No part of this publication may be reproduced, stored in any retrieval system, or transmitted in any form by any means, including electronic, mechanical, photocopying, recording or otherwise, without the prior written consent of the publisher.

DISCLAIMER

Whilst every effort has been made to ensure that this book provides accurate information, it is impossible to predict all the circumstances in which it may be used. The author, publisher, and retailer cannot be held liable to any person or entity with respect to any loss or damage caused by, or allegedly caused by, the information contained in this book.

This book is not a substitute for making a Will. Passing away without leaving a Will is almost certain to make it more difficult for those you leave behind to deal with your affairs.

Some names contained within the Foreword have been changed.

Typeset in 12pt Sabon by Troubador Publishing Ltd, Leicester, UK
Printed and bound by TJ International Ltd, Padstow, Cornwall, UK

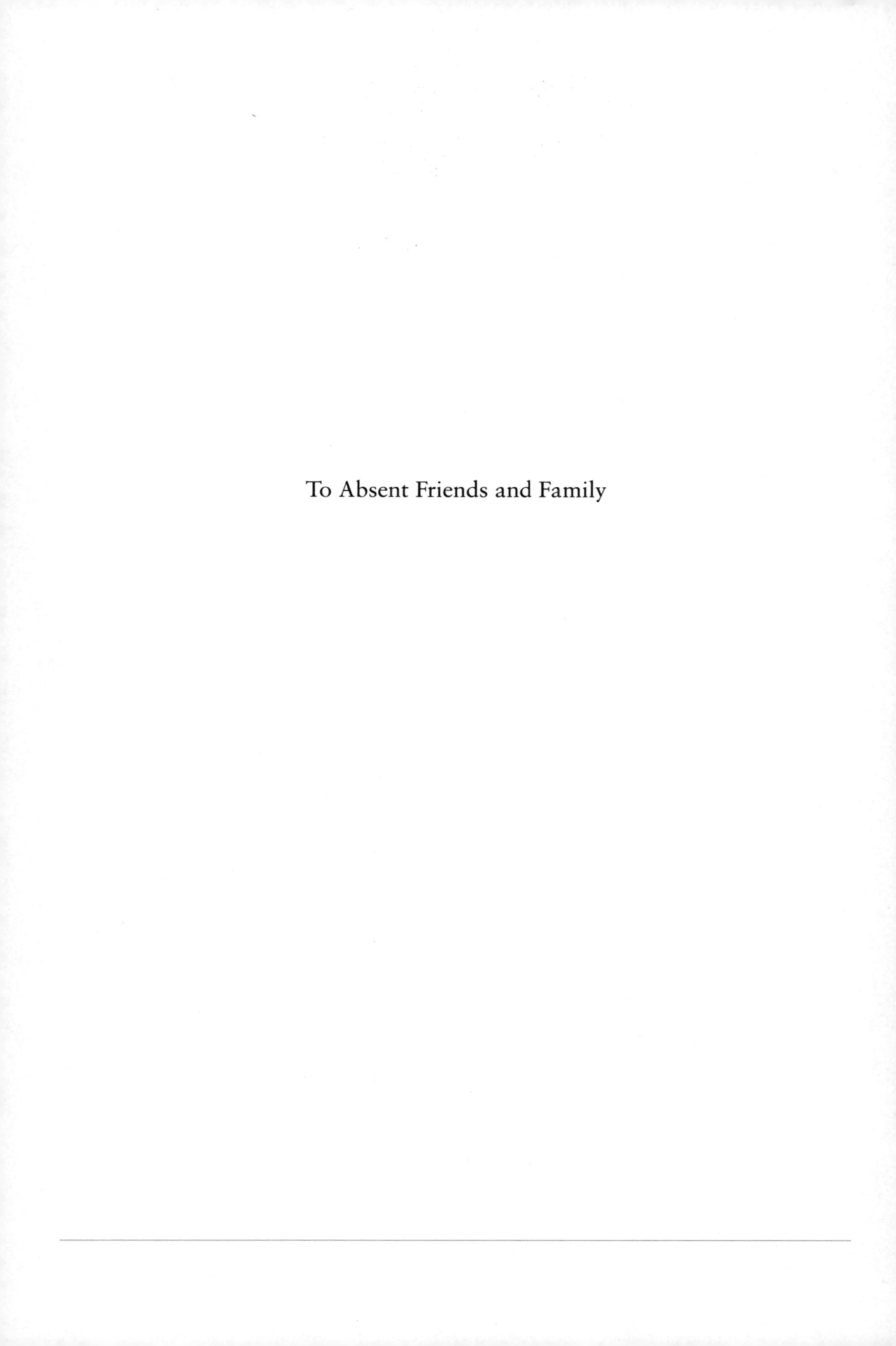

To Absent Friends and Family

LAST ORDERS

The Essential Guide to

_________________________ 's

Letter of Wishes

(Please complete)

Contents

Acknowledgements

Who is to say why one idea remains dormant, never to see the light of day, and why another flies? The intricacies and coincidences contained within our daily lives, of haphazard events and random meetings, which for most, go largely unnoticed, are forever weaving the fabric of our lives and shaping our future as the gods tinker with our destiny.

So it was in March 2009, a series of events occurred to make me revisit the dormant notes which I wrote in 2006 for a friend who was dying. In bringing the notes to light, it is almost as if they took on a life of their own. Further unplanned meetings and chance conversations with those who had similar experiences to my own, started to fuel the project.

As I continued to review and add to the content to the book I received much needed and appreciated encouragement to publish it, notably from my sister Marie Nicholson and my brother Michael Bracken who have shown nothing but loyalty and friendship under life's most trying circumstances. I am indebted too, to my wider family for the support they continue to offer, notably Joe Martin in Ireland for his own special brand of Irish wit and his insight, Sister Antoninus Martin in the U.S. who offers encouragement and spirituality to everything I undertake, and to the inimitable Terry Buegg in London for her unfailing optimism and faith in me.

If ever a time came when I doubted the importance of the little book, something or someone came along in random fashion to lend support, and show guidance. I refer to very kind gentlemen such as the outstanding Gary Wicks in London, and John Frawley in Poland who have both shown remarkable generosity of spirit at a time when it was very much needed. Last, but in no way least, sincere and special thanks must go to my personal advisor and lawyer, Tim Bullimore to whom I will be forever indebted. All of which suggests the gods are benevolently showering nothing but good things over this corner of Cheshire these days.

Foreword

Since writing *Last Orders*, I have been constantly asked what brought me to the point where I felt the need to assemble it. Sadly, I can only answer it was because of the difficulties I have witnessed and the trials I have had to face. Taking time to write this book in the hope that it will shed some light on a much neglected subject seemed a small price to pay if it meant that others would not have to endure the same...

In 2003, my dear friend Maria died of breast cancer, aged 49. She was single, without children, with an elderly housebound parent, and brothers she rarely saw. Her support network was her few close friends and I was one of her closest, with us having been friends for many years. We had cried together when she discovered she had the disease in 1999 and I stayed close by her throughout the entire duration of her illness from diagnosis, through her scans, her operations and the endless courses of chemotherapy she underwent, until the day she died.

Maria was a strong, vibrant lady full of vitality; she firmly believed she would recover from the disease, and so never wished to face the prospect of death. On just one occasion, a few weeks before she died, I attempted to discuss with her what she would want if the worst happened, but she clearly did not wish to even consider it, so many questions were left unanswered.

After four years of battling the cancer, Maria sadly passed away at home. In spite of attempts to keep calm throughout those last days, I was in deep shock when she died having never had to deal with a life-threatening illness at such close quarters. Just hours after her death, I was asked by the funeral director to search through Maria's wardrobe to find an outfit for the undertaker to dress her. I felt distraught and helpless; I chastised myself endlessly for not having done more, or for ensuring her Last Orders were in place whilst she was alive.

In spite of the severity of her illness and her prognosis, Maria had left a Will so outdated that it bore no relation to the situation she was in. Nor were there any instructions for her funeral, so it took on the same pattern as her father's which had occurred just six months earlier. Whilst this was a lovely service, it bore none of her characteristic cheerfulness, nor was it a reflection of the vibrant globetrotter she had been. Later, when I assisted in clearing her property, her belongings were distributed to friends and relatives with some angst and even confusion. To this day, I believe I could have and should have done more to help her make those tough decisions which would have smoothed the difficulties which surrounded her death.

Sadly, a year before Maria died, a second friend, Kate, was also diagnosed with the same disease. In 2006, as Kate's health started to fail, she asked me to be the executor of her Will. Similar to Maria, she was also a single lady, without children, hugely bright with a wicked sense of humour. She, too, had no family she could call on and although popular, was an intensely private individual so I knew it would be down to the executors to handle not just her estate after her death, but to cope with the final weeks of her life too.

Knowing some of the issues which had been raised by Maria's death, and the endless angst which I experienced afterwards, it prompted me to write *Last Orders* for Kate. I pre-warned her on the 'phone before giving her a copy, so she was the first to see it. Even then, it shocked her. Many tears were shed between us as she completed it, but it was important to me that she understood that I was only asking such difficult questions because I had been through similar issues with Maria, whom we both missed immensely. It was my desire, even my need, to do the right thing for her – including anything and everything surrounding her death, her funeral, her belongings and not least, her beloved chocolate labrador, Coco. Fair play to Kate, once she understood my reasoning, she laughed with gusto and her black humour entered into the spirit of the book by answering my searching questions with some very colourful replies (which are unprintable!). In the last days of her life, at her bedside, she was still reading the notes I had made and we, together, altered her funeral requests.

When the dreadful time came, and Kate passed peacefully away at home, her requests were adhered to; to the letter. Her funeral was truly wonderful, with Coco as chief mourner who whimpered throughout the entire service. Many of the congregation said it was the best funeral they had ever been to. What was heart-warming was that, in spite of very difficult circumstances, everything went without a single hitch. I have much to thank Sue Clarke, the co-executrix, friends Lesley Nesbitt and Chrissie Westbrook for support throughout those difficult days, but, of course, especially to Kate for her willingness to complete the book.

Feeling somewhat self-satisfied that Kate's funeral had been orchestrated with such success, I mentioned the book to my mother, Kit, as I was also executor of her Will. Kit, a larger than life vivacious lady, sadly, did not accept it with the same willingness that Kate did. In fact, she did not wish to complete it at all. So the book was forgotten and lay dormant on my computer.

When Kit died suddenly in 2008, the entire family was sent into extreme shock, and we were all quite traumatised. She had made her Will, but this time, there was no book to refer to, and therefore no information outlining her wishes surrounding her funeral, or her belongings. She and I had discussed, over the years, the merits of various funerals we had attended, and so I believed I knew some of what she would have wanted. However, coming from a large family, everyone believed they knew what she would have wanted. This led to many disagreements about her funeral, her flowers, her gravestone, her belongings... the list was endless. To add fuel to the fire, whilst her Will addressed the distribution of her estate, complications arose which did nothing to calm very troubled waters within the family.

Now on reflection, I put much of the confrontation that ensued down to family members' profound grief and an inability to handle the loss of a deeply loved and cherished mother. Time and time again I wish I had been stronger when asking her to complete the book, which would have eased the loss, and brought clarity to the confusion. Instead, even as executor, each step in administering her estate was excruciating, protracted, and distressing for all concerned. It is for this reason that I have written *Last Orders* so that others will not have to endure the same.

All families are capable of falling out. For those who take the moral high ground and believe that they and their family are above such tribulations, I truly hope such optimism and tranquillity prevails. For the rest of us, and for those who are unwilling to even risk such a thing, I remain hopeful that this book will help you and your family.

I am the first to acknowledge it does not make for pleasant reading and I fully expect you will have the same initial reaction as Kate did. However, believe me, when the time comes and the book is needed by your executors, you will be posthumously thanked endlessly for the foresight you had in completing it.

My aim is to keep the book and the website (www.lastorders.org) as simple as possible but I remain open to comments from anyone. All of my suggestions, questions and observations were borne from my very different experiences of funerals and the administering of estates, but chiefly from the lessons learnt from Maria, Kate and Kit who continue to keep me busy... even now.

With very best wishes

Patricia

Introduction

Good Willing...

This book is intended to assist anyone and everyone. It is not a Will and nor should it be considered as such. It is however, something which, once completed correctly, should save incalculable amounts of stress and take most, if not all, of the guesswork out of making arrangements following a death and in the administration of an estate. Whilst a Will centres on the deceased's finances and possessions, this book, which will serve as a Letter of Wishes, deals with the more intimate aspects of passing and caters for fundamental issues which have to be addressed on a more practical and personal level. What is crucial is to recognise that the content of this book is applicable to everyone, regardless of age.

In reading and completing *Last Orders*, you are assisting those you leave behind by generously and selflessly addressing one of the most difficult issues which we will all have to deal with: that is death. Whilst this is extremely uncomfortable to consider, there can be few kinder acts than actively taking steps to make your passing as stress-free as possible for those you leave behind; the people you care about most. They are likely to be in shock, distressed, and grieving at their loss. Making decisions at such a time, surrounding not just your funeral but events before and after it, can be tremendously stressful and traumatic. In supplying them with answers to most, or all, of those questions, you are taking away confusion and relieving them of untold amounts of guesswork. Therefore the aim of this book is to eliminate doubt and offer clarity.

There are some who will consider a book and a subject matter such as this not worthy of their consideration. In taking that stance, they are effectively not prepared to give thought to those left behind or to the ensuing trials which may accompany their passing. The unwillingness to face the subject of death, which is the greatest inevitability of one's life, could be seen as indifference for those who are, apparently, their 'nearest and dearest'. Equally, assuming an air of apathy and leaving someone else to deal with matters could be seen, not only as irresponsible, but gives little consideration to the state of grief that their 'nearest and dearest' will be in. Anything that any of us can do to ease some of that distress is not only sensible but highly commendable.

As previously mentioned, this book is not a Will, and the contents and requests you make within it are not legally binding. However, hopefully your executors, and those you leave behind, will be happy to honour and feel morally obliged, to follow these Last Orders as far as practically possible. Executors sometimes have to make difficult and controversial decisions, so if the content of this book, and the answers you supply, can do anything to ease that difficulty, and enlighten others as to what your Last Orders were, then it could ease a lot of unnecessary tension. Indeed, your executors are likely to be extremely grateful for the assistance you have offered in supplying the answers.

Before addressing the content of the book, it is important that you take the necessary steps, if you have not already done so, of protecting your loved ones and your assets, by making a Will. With today's complicated lifestyles, partnership and marriage break-ups, having a Will in place brings a level of certainty as to how your estate – that is your property, your finances, and your belongings – will be distributed after your death. Who receives anything, and to what level they do, is entirely down to the instructions and wishes documented in your Will. Equally important, and somewhat ironically, it seems that many people write a Will to ensure that certain people *have no claim* on their estate.

If you die and, for whatever reason, have not made a Will, your estate will be distributed according to the law which, in itself, may not correspond at any level with how you would have chosen to allocate your finances and possessions. Relying on the rules of intestacy (that is dying without a Will in place) to distribute your money can, at best, be seen as precarious, and at worst irresponsible. Intestacy brings many difficult issues to the fore; and whilst this is not the book to explore all the variances, there are some myths to dispel. It may, for example, be worth noting that, in England, without a Will in place, if you have children, the most your spouse can inherit from you is capped at £250,000 and thereafter, residue funds have constraints placed upon them. Also, a separated spouse, from whom you are not yet divorced, can make a claim on your estate whilst a co-habitee cannot. So, unless provision is made for a live-in partner in your Will, they could be homeless as well as partner-less within a few weeks of your death whilst your separated spouse makes their claim. Furthermore, your estate may be liable to pay Inheritance Tax which could have been avoided with some legitimate and proper tax planning.

There are a number of avenues you can take to make a Will from DIY Will kits, to companies which claim to specialise in Will-making and, of course, via a solicitor. Over-the-counter Will kits and downloadable versions are a low-cost option, which offer an unrivalled immediacy to the Will-making process. However, whilst they may be suitable in the most straight-forward of circumstances, you must be advised that if completed incorrectly, a sorry mess can ensue leaving part or all of the Will invalid which, in itself, can lead to expensive and stressful complications. The Society of Trust and Estate Practitioners, (www.step.org/findapractitioner) a world-wide professional body which oversees trusts, estates and legacies, states that one of the most common mistakes in DIY Wills is that the Will-maker fails to cover for the possibility that the main beneficiary does not survive them. STEP has collated many examples where the results have been, in their words, "disastrous".

Similarly, there are companies which purport to specialise in Will writing, and which may, on the face of it, appear to be a convenient way to make one's Will as consultants visit potential Will-makers in their homes. However, according to the Law Society, (www.lawsociety.org.uk) the public are being exposed to "unregulated, unqualified and uninsured Will writers" when using some of these companies. Some advertise low-cost Wills, particularly in local newspapers, enticing prospective clients who find, once hidden charges such as Will-storage costs are added, end up with a ludicrously expensive bill. This can actually end up being costlier than using a bona-fide firm of solicitors, some of which do not charge for Will storage at all. It has also been found that some Will-making consultants have gone so far as to appoint themselves as executors to clients Wills which can, in itself, be highly lucrative for the consultant. Such practice is far from rare. It should also be noted that some of these companies are lacking in professional indemnity insurance, so you are unlikely to be offered any form of redress if a Will has been incorrectly drafted. According to the Law Society, solicitors have collated many cases of people who have "turned to them for help after being left with what can only be described as nightmare Wills by Will writers, many of which are not worth the paper they are written on."

Sadly, and crucially, errors which are made in either of the aforementioned processes are usually only discovered on application for Probate, when it is too late to resolve them. In such circumstances the Will would then be deemed to be useless and the law would have to decide how your estate would be distributed. Therefore, if you have already chosen to make your Will with either of the above processes, it is strongly recommended that you get it checked by a solicitor or a member of STEP whilst you still have the ability to remedy any mistakes which could create problems for your loved ones in the future.

Having looked at two of the options for making your Will, and with all things considered, there really can be no better solution than consulting with a solicitor for a professional, water-tight Will which leaves nothing to chance. Solicitors are legally qualified, robustly regulated, and are covered by insurance for the rare occasion when some form of recompense is required. So, they have the advantage of having all angles covered, as indeed will you, having made the wise decision to entrust a professional to deal with your valuable assets.

In spite of this appearing, on the face of it, to be the most expensive option in monetary terms, it could and should ultimately save your beneficiaries time – inasmuch as the Will should receive Probate without any difficulty; money – if your solicitor has advised you on Inheritance Tax – and most importantly, should save an inordinate amount of stress from the muddle that can ensue from some of the other Will-making options.

It may be useful to note that there are certain times annually, when solicitors offer promotional Will-making campaigns to incentivise us all into making our Will. There is an annual campaign organised by Will-Aid which runs for the month of November, when participating solicitors can draw up a new Will, oversee an existing Will, or even add a codicil (an amendment to an existing Will). In doing so, the solicitors waive their fees and invite you to donate it to a Will-Aid charity instead, ensuring funds are raised for exceptional work throughout the world. For further information and participating solicitors visit www.willaid.org.uk. If you are over the age of 55 and are prepared to make a donation in your Will to their charity, Cancer Research UK will pay for a standard Will to be drawn up under their Free Will Service. The amount you choose to donate is discretionary. For further information on the scheme you may wish to visit the website www.cancerresearchuk.org/legacies.

Clearly the complexity and size of your estate will, more than likely, determine which Will-making avenue you choose. Someone with three ex-wives in tow, and children scattered liberally throughout the country, will have different priorities and needs to a single, childless person, and the cost of tailoring one's Will to encompass such differences will vary accordingly. Whichever option you choose, it is important that you review your Will from time to time to ensure that its content is still relevant. It is recommended that this is done around every five years, or when your circumstances change.

When making a Will, you will need to choose executors, who may or may not be beneficiaries. They will carry out your wishes and administer your estate in line with your Will and the law. Most people choose to have two people they know well as their executors (although up to four is permissible). What is important is that you choose executors who are trustworthy, morally sound, have the time, the skills and the wherewithal to deal with the myriad of problems which can arise and who, most importantly, are happy to take on the responsibility. Equally important, and rarely commented upon, is the need for your executors to have some kind of rapport; there is little to be gained in appointing two people who find it impossible to agree on anything. There can be significant and sometimes difficult decisions to make surrounding your estate so a meeting of minds is crucial. There is also a lot of documentation to deal with, so your executors should be used to administrative work. Finally, they should also have a level of integrity which ensures that, as much as is practical, the wishes stated within this book are adhered to.

You may wish to appoint your solicitor to act as your executor and there are many advantages in doing so. A solicitor should bring a level of expertise to the administration of an estate which may be helpful if your Will is particularly complex or contentious, or which could overstretch the skills of a non-professional executor. Similarly, a solicitor is likely to be highly experienced in liquidating estates, and should know all the procedures to recoup any money due to the estate – not least from the taxman. Finally, and importantly, a solicitor will release the non-professional executor from being liable for any mistakes which are made during the course of settling the estate. You should, however, be aware that a non-professional executor will have limited control over the administration of your estate if a solicitor is chosen as joint executor. Also, it can prove costly so you should check the rates your solicitor will charge for the service. By contrast, non-professional executors can only charge your estate for out-of-pocket expenses, not for any of the time they spend during the course of the administration.

Some solicitors may lack the personal touch which is highlighted and required in the following pages, so it is important that they familiarise themselves with the more personal aspects of your life. This can be resolved simply by ensuring this book is completed and ensuring your solicitor, if an executor, has a copy. There are numerous excellent websites and books which address the role of an executor and the responsibilities entailed in administering an estate after a death, so this book will not repeat them. The fundamental difference is that *Last Orders* seeks to attain answers to pertinent questions *before* death takes place.

There are many different aspects surrounding death covered in the following pages on a wide variety of subjects. Some observations and questions have specifically been included in an attempt to encourage you to think about issues which you may have, up until now, avoided. Indeed, one of the book's chief aims is to prompt you into seeking specialist advice in any area you feel is necessary and relevant to you. This book, no matter how well-intentioned, cannot address all the issues in depth, nor take into account all the vagaries of every person's circumstances. So, if you are in any doubt about any of the topics raised and feel you need specialist advice, it is strongly recommended that you seek further guidance in any of the specific fields.

When reading the following sections, you will read some thought-provoking questions. These will need answers from you, about you, about – not least – the funeral you would wish for, the distribution of your belongings and all aspects which will need to be addressed after your death.

Wherever there is a question mark followed by a grey box, complete it as necessary. It is advisable to use ink or a ballpoint, using block capital handwriting, and sign and date the last page. Notes have been inserted in boxes for assistance, offering background information and suggestions.

Please be aware that some questions listed are difficult to address. They are even more difficult to answer, but those answers will assist hugely in ensuring that your last requests are known and carried out to the letter, which is the ultimate aim. Not least, by giving clear answers you will have contributed greatly to making your passing as peaceful as possible for those remaining.

You can complete as little or as much of the book as you wish and the choices you make will, in itself, demonstrate to your executors the issues which are important to you. For example, you may not wish to answer questions about certain aspects of your funeral, but may merely wish to state your preference for the music which is to be played. Or you may wish to let it be known, in the Goods and Chattels section for example, that the picture that is currently above the fireplace with the tatty frame was actually painted by your great, great grandfather, that Dorothy at number 23 has a spare set of keys to your house and that, in the Pets section, your cat is allergic to chicken.

In answering any of the questions please bear in mind that it is not sufficient to say that a partner knows this or X knows that. Consideration should be given to the emotional state that a partner or X may be in. Additionally, there must be ample information in case a situation arises where neither a partner, nor X, is available.

The format of the book has been kept simple. The sizing of the pages ensures it is easy to write on, with sufficient space to write your response. Throughout the book there are pages which have intentionally been left blank for any additional information you may wish to supply. If amendments or additions are made at any time, you may wish to date any alterations so that it is clear which is your preferred answer.

As with making a Will, it is important to review the content of the book from time to time to ensure that it is still a true representation of your wishes. There are several blank pages at the back for your own notes and additions. Finally, once the answers have been completed, (and it need not all be done in one sitting), it is crucial that you put the book somewhere safe, preferably alongside your Will, and that you tell your executors where to find it.

SECTION ONE

Contacts

The first task any executor has to undertake is to inform relatives, friends and colleagues of your passing. If one considers that this is likely to take place on the very day of your death, when they are likely to be in a state of shock and very distressed, just knowing whom to contact can ease the situation tremendously.

Finding an old address book or a much used Filofax may, at first, seem to be useful, but who is to say how current and relevant the names are? An executor making telephone calls to people he or she does not know, to tell them of the death of someone they have not seen or heard from in 20 years, is difficult and extremely upsetting for all concerned.

Consider keeping your Christmas card list or the list of attendees of any annual reunion. This will show those people with whom you are in touch ... even if it is only on a once a year basis.

If there is such a list, where would you keep it?

So, the first thing you can do to assist, is to supply a list of all those you wish to have notified of your passing. This list need not be extensive – perhaps only one or two per group of friends or colleagues who can, in turn, relate the news to others. This will greatly assist any person who has the sad task of contacting those close to you. Alternatively, you may choose to leave an existing address book with the names, addresses and contact details of those you wish to be informed, highlighted with a marker pen, or with a discreet star, tick or letter next to the name.

If this is more convenient and the preferred choice, where within your property do you keep your address book and how will you mark the people to contact?

Similarly, consider: is it easy enough to log onto your computer and your email address book to find who you are in touch with on the internet? You may wish to leave any codes or passwords with your executor, or in a safe place.

Your executors will have to inform any social networking sites you are on, such as Facebook, Twitter, Myspace so what is/are your user name(s) and passwords?

There is a list on page 3, so that you can write down the names of those you wish to be contacted.

Executors:
You may have to offer social networking sites some form of 'proof' of death by submitting an obituary, news article or death certificate. Accounts can remain open in memory of the deceased but with limited access if desired.

CONTACTS

CONTACT	TELEPHONE NOS	EMAIL ADDRESS	DONE ✓
EMPLOYER			
DOCTOR			
DENTIST			
LANDLORD			

Page intentionally left blank for your notes

Before a funeral can take place, a death must be registered with the Registrar. The person registering your death, either a close relative residing in the area or one attending at the time of death, will need to produce some information about you. It may be useful to put some of this information at the back of this book.

They will need the Medical Certificate detailing the cause of death (signed by a doctor) either a normal GP or a hospital doctor if the death occurred in hospital. They will also need to provide details of the date & place of death.

It is possible, and advisable, to obtain extra copies of the Death Certificate; there will be additional charges for this. Each insurance company, bank, and financial body will require sight of an original copy before releasing funds and it may take time for each organisation to return originals.

For the sake of completeness, and to assist your executors, please complete the following questions:

Your full name: ______________________________

Your full address: ______________________________

____

____

Your maiden name (if applicable) ______________________________

Your date and place of birth: ______________________________

Your occupation: ______________________________

The location of your medical card: ______________________________

The location of your birth certificate: ______________________________

The location of your Marriage/Civil Partnership Certificate: ______________________________

Details of pension or allowances coming from the government: ______________________________

____

Page intentionally left blank for your notes

SECTION TWO

The Funeral

The arrangement of your funeral or memorial service, and the choices made surrounding it, are intensely personal and should be an expression of the life you have led. Ideally it should reflect your tastes, your own special wishes, and leave those attending it in no doubt about your place in the world. For this reason, it should go without saying that the very best person to arrange it is you.

However if you have not chosen, nor wish to choose, the various elements of your own service, you may wish to elect someone else to make arrangements on your behalf; later in this section you can state who should do that. The alternative is to leave it to your family. Whilst this can be useful, it should be noted that if there are several people in the mix, they may or may not agree on issues, which can cause considerable distress to all. Therefore, if you can eliminate the potential of disagreements by

You may wish to consider opting for a pre-paid funeral, whereby you pay for and make your own funeral arrangements ahead of time. The advantages of this are:
a) You will get the funeral you would wish for
b) It will free the executors of being liable for the cost of the funeral and
c) Your funeral will be paid for at today's prices.

making your own arrangements, it would be to everyone's benefit.

Funerals and memorial services can be expensive and are generally costly affairs. Options for transportation range from the hire of a single hearse to horse-drawn carriages; floral tributes range from single roses to wreaths which can cover the entire coffin in any shape or style you prefer; coffins range from "green" eco-friendly cardboard to oak caskets. It is important, therefore, that you choose the level of expense which is manageable to your estate and that you are aware of the costs before making any decisions. You should also bear in mind that your executors can be liable for the cost of your funeral.

Funeral directors often have different levels of service (such as basic, medium and deluxe) and prices vary accordingly. Likewise, their chapels of rest vary in quality and may be another factor worthy of consideration. Some are quite luxurious with marble floors, lit candles and fresh flowers; others look like something from a 1960's sit-com, complete with swirly patterned carpets and artificial flowers. There is nothing wrong with the latter, except that it should, perhaps, be reflected in the prices of the funeral services which are offered.

Funeral directors are experienced in all stages of planning a funeral and should provide a professional one-stop shop for all your funereal needs. From flowers, to the printing of the Order of Service, to the after service refreshments; all can be organised through your undertaker. It should be noted, however, that this service comes at a price and you may wish to purchase the items listed above, (amongst other key ingredients) elsewhere. Prices between funeral directors range hugely, and you may wish to take the opportunity to get quotes in writing from various sources before deciding whom to use.

Generally speaking, making the decision about which option to choose becomes more difficult after a death, when poor decisions can be made as a result of grief, shock and a need to be seen to be "doing the right thing", which is perhaps another reason to put some instructions in place ahead of time.

In the age of "every option is available," and if you have no spiritual or religious faith, you may also wish to consider whether you would prefer a Civil Funeral

Service. Many undertakers offer this option, and the service can be personalised through tributes from family and friends.

Whether you prefer a traditional funeral with hymns, a memorial service with a more contemporary slant or a Civil Funeral Service with its various options, it may also be worth considering those you leave behind. Some kind of service, no matter how austere, may offer more comfort and closure than others for mourners.

So, with this in mind, what is your preferred choice?

A Civil Funeral Service is a dignified ceremony which reflects the beliefs and values of the deceased, and is predominantly non-religious. It is often highly personalised with family members and friends taking an active role via readings, poetry, and songs which reflect the deceased's life. It can take place almost anywhere other than a religious building. Anyone can conduct such a ceremony, although there are Civil Funeral Service celebrants who are trained and skilled in such matters.

When completing the following questions, remember that it is important that you answer what you feel comfortable with, and equally important that you state on the following pages anything that you *do not want to include* in your funeral.

1. Have you chosen or considered which funeral services you wish to use? If so, please supply details of name, address and telephone number:

2. If not, do you wish your family, or your executors (if not one and the same) to choose which company to use and to arrange the details of your funeral? Please specify who should choose:

3. If you have pre-paid for your funeral, where is the documentation to prove this?

4. The cost of your funeral will (most likely) come out of your estate, but you should be mindful that your executors can be held liable for the funeral account. If choices have to be made on your behalf, on a scale of 1 to 10, with 1 being the least expensive and 10 the most expensive, how much do you wish to spend?

5. Do you wish your coffin to be carried in a hearse?

If not, what is your preferred alternative and where can it be found?

Note that although it is traditional for a hearse to be used, it is by no means compulsory. For example, an ambulance driver was carried to his grave in an ambulance; a lorry driver in his lorry, and founder of the Body Shop Anita Roddick, opted for a camper van to be used as her hearse ... so alternatives are available.

6. Please specify whether you wish your family and friends to be transported in limousines. If so, how many and who should use them?

7. Do you have any preference as to the route which is taken to the funeral?

8. Have you purchased or chosen a coffin? If so, where is it? Who knows about this?

9. If not, do you have any preference as to the colour or design?

10. Following your passing, do you wish to be embalmed?

11. Following your passing, do you wish for mourners to be able to view your remains?

Embalming is purely for cosmetic effect, and should you prefer for your remains not to be viewed, there is little to be gained in requesting, and paying for, the process. The procedure should be optional and if it is not required, it is important that your executors advise the funeral director accordingly.

If the answer is yes, is there anyone you wish to exclude from being able to do this?

12. Have you considered anything which you wish to be placed in your coffin alongside you? Please list:

It is customary, although not essential, to place mementos in the coffin. Items can be of sentimental value, or intensely personal such as letters written to the deceased.

The range of favoured items is huge. Money is popular as is food, sweets, mobile 'phones and cigarettes. Frank Sinatra's assortment of items for his coffin is legendary.

If the burial is to take place in a natural burial site there may be restrictions on items which can be placed in the coffin (all items must be bio-degradable and eco-friendly). Similarly, there are certain items which cannot be included should you opt for a cremation.

It is advisable to check with the funeral director as to what is permitted.

13. Do you permanently wear any item(s) of jewellery?

14. Would you wish this/these item(s) to be buried with your remains?

15. Or have you bequeathed these items to individuals in your Will?

Please specify which item(s) and to whom:

16. Have you considered what clothes you wish to be buried in?

17. Do you wish for a notice of your passing to be placed in any newspaper's Obituaries column?

If so, which newspaper(s)?

The choice of clothes to wear is often varied and down to the individual.

Some ladies wear their wedding dress, others wear their Sunday best, a favourite outfit or pyjamas and bed socks.

If all else fails, funeral directors can supply gowns or shrouds which can be used, but they are not inexpensive.

18. Is there anything particular you would wish to have mentioned within the Obituary?

19. Do you have any particular likes or dislikes regarding the flowers which are used? (Colour/type/arrangement?)

What kind of wreath(s) would you prefer (if any)?

20. Would you prefer mourners to send flowers or donate to a charity? If the latter, which charity/charities?

With this in mind, do you wish there to be a collection as mourners leave the service?

Or would you prefer some other form of commemoration such as a bench or plaque?
And where would you want such a commemoration to be placed?

21. Prior to your funeral, would you wish for a Requiem Mass the evening before?

Options for what happens the day prior to your funeral can be considered and although Requiem Masses and wakes are becoming increasingly unusual, they are by no means rare.

22. Alternatively, would you wish for your coffin and your remains to return home for the night before your funeral?

23. Where do you wish your memorial service or funeral to be held?

24. Do you wish to have a private service and burial for close family and friends only?

25. Who would you prefer to hold the Service? (Perhaps a particular priest/minister?)

26. Thinking about your coffin – do you have any preference as to who the pallbearers would be? Please list: (*Note: Six to eight are required.*)

Equally important, is there someone you would rather not be a pallbearer?

27. Once inside the place of worship, is there anything you would like placed on top of your coffin?

28. Have you any preferences as to what readings or poems are read at the service? Please list what they are and where they can be found.

You may wish to write out the readings overleaf.

Many places of worship will not permit flags to drape the coffin – ie the Union flag, Tricolor etc.

However, many mourners place a photograph of the deceased on top of the coffin, and flowers are always popular. Items which were familiar to the deceased are particularly touching and evocative. (Such as a garden trowel, the Racing Post, a pipe, a racing helmet, military paraphernalia etc...)

There are many options for readings from religious text to contemporary poetry. There is not sufficient space to list them in full here, but there are ample examples to choose from on the internet at: www.rememberlife.com

It may be useful to leave details of where your chosen readings can be found if they are particularly unusual.

Page intentionally left blank for your notes

29. The choice of music you make for the service or mass will create the tone and set the mood. Whether you wish it to be solemn and traditional, or more upbeat and a celebration of your life is entirely up to you. Options abound and can include everything from bagpipes, to a vocalist, to tracks from CDs. This is a very personal matter, and one which others cannot easily choose. You may also need to bear in mind whether a contemporary twist on a traditional funeral is acceptable to some clergy. Consider too, whether you want mourners to weep buckets of tears, or leave the service with a smile on their face.

So, what are your preferences for music or hymns to be played at the service? Please list.

There are many options for music. The top 10 contemporary song choices are:

1. *Goodbye My Lover*
2. *Angels*
3. *I've Had the time of my Life*
4. *Wind beneath My Wings*
5. *Candle in the Wind*
6. *With or Without You*
7. *Tears in Heaven*
8. *Every Breath You Take*
9. *Unchained Melody*
10. *Time to Say Goodbye*

The top 10 Hymn Choices:

1. *The Lord is my Shepherd*
2. *Abide With Me*
3. *All things bright & beautiful*
4. *Old Rugged Cross*
5. *Amazing Grace*
6. *How Great Thou Art*
7. *The Day Thou gaveth, Lord*
8. *Jerusalem*
9. *Make me a Channel*
10. *Morning has broken*

The top 10 Classical:

1. *Nimrod*
2. *Ave Maria*
3. *Nessun Dorma*
4. *Pie Jesu*
5. *Canon in D*
6. *Jesu, Joy of Man's desiring*
7. *Air on a G String*
8. *Going Home*
9. *The Four Seasons*
10. *Largo from Xerxes*

Page intentionally left blank for your notes

30. In terms of the mourners, do you have any special wishes as to whether they are dressed in traditional black or would you prefer a more colourful affair? Please supply details:

31. Do you have any preference as to whom should carry out the eulogy?

32. In order to assist the eulogist, are there any pointers you would like mentioned? *Consider: your achievements, career, hobbies, memberships of clubs/societies, people in your life, amusing stories...etc.*

33. Having chosen the music and the readings, please list the Order of Service which you would prefer (if any particular order). Consider perhaps the Entrance music, the order of readings you would prefer, mid-service music, the eulogy, and music to leave the service to.
(Note: the following is only a suggestion. Modify your own version as you see fit)

Entrance Music ______________________

Introduction ______________________

Reading 1 ______________________

Music ______________________

Reading 2 ______________________

Music ______________________

Eulogy ______________________

The Commendation ______________________

Music to leave to ______________________

34. Do you wish to be buried or cremated?
If the former you should go to Page 27 or Page 31 for the latter.

Over two-thirds of funerals in the UK are followed by cremations, with less than one third now opting for burials.

In the UK, cremation is the less expensive of the two.

Page intentionally left blank for your notes

Page intentionally left blank for your notes

SECTION THREE

Grave Thoughts...

There are a number of options available if one is considering a burial. Plots in cemeteries and churchyards range considerably in price depending on the location. You should also be aware that a burial plot is merely leased to you for a number of years and those leases vary in length. So, you may wish to check the costs and the duration of the leases in nearby cemeteries before deciding. Having selected the cemetery, you may also wish to choose where within it you wish to be buried. Some prefer plots next to the pathways, making it easier to visit, or near a bench. These often are slightly more expensive.

Natural, Woodland or Green Burial Grounds are becoming increasingly popular and are seen as an environmentally friendly and an alternative option for those who aren't religious. There are a number of considerations to take into account, such as coffin type, the fact that no headstones can be mounted, and that there are often restrictions as to what types of plants, shrubs and bulbs which can be planted in memory of a loved one. As such burial grounds are still relatively sparse nationwide, you may need to research the location of such sites.

Whilst the customary place of burial is a cemetery, alternatives are available. Burial at sea is an option (although there are some legalities to take into consideration).

1. Which cemetery do you wish to be buried in?

2. Have you purchased a plot, or is there an existing plot available to you?

Do you have the documentation required to verify this and where is it?

What is the plot number?

3. Have you considered whether you would like a headstone? If so, which type?

4. Is there anything you wish to omit from the headstone?

The choice of epitaph on a headstone can be thought provoking and even pithy. Frank Sinatra's has "The Best is yet to Come" on his headstone. Well documented is the epitaph requested by Irish born and former Goon Spike Milligan who wanted the inscription "I told you I was ill" on his headstone. However, the Diocese of Chichester, where his grave is, had issues with the request. Instead his family agreed to inscribe the epitaph in Gaelic.

What inscription do you wish to have?

5. At the final interment, that is, the graveside, do you wish anything special to happen?

It is becoming increasingly popular for music to be played at the graveside. You may wish to consider this.
Similarly, balloons or even doves are sometimes released at the end of the graveside service.

SECTION FOUR

Cremation

If you have chosen to be cremated you may wish to consider what you would like to happen to your ashes. Whether you choose to have them buried somewhere special, scattered or kept in a special urn can be decided upon in advance. It may be something you wish to discuss with your loved ones.

There are many options as to where ashes can be scattered, from the Remembrance Gardens in a crematorium, to a cemetery or to a favourite location although you should bear in mind that permission must be sought from the landowner before scattering in certain areas.

Star Trek creator Gene Roddenberry and actor James Doohan, who played Scottie in the cult TV series, both had their ashes sent into outer space. If that is a bridge too far, ashes can be put into fireworks which guarantee a spectacular and different event.

There are woodland sites which specialise in the burying of ashes alongside the planting of a tree. Some football grounds even allow a place for ashes to be buried within the grounds.

1. Do you have any preference as to which crematorium is used?

2. What do you wish to happen to your ashes?

3. If you wish your ashes to be scattered, please say where:

Following the burial or scattering of your ashes, do you wish mourners to celebrate your life in any way at that point? Please say how:

4. You may choose to erect a plaque at a cemetery or a crematorium. If so, where would be your preference?

5. What inscription do you wish to have?
Equally important, is there anything you wish to omit from the plaque?

Page intentionally left blank for your notes

SECTION FIVE

After Thoughts...

1. Have you considered whether you would wish for the mourners to meet after the funeral? If so, where?

2. Do you have any preferences as to what is served after the funeral?
   If so, please specify:

3. Do you have any further wishes or requests whatsoever regarding your funeral?

Page intentionally left blank for your notes

SECTION SIX

Medical Matters

1. Have you registered as an organ donor?

Or do you carry a donor card? Where is it?

Choosing to donate your body's organs after your death can mean the difference between life and death for someone else. It can prove to be life-enhancing for many more. Age is not a barrier to donating or receiving an organ. The oldest recipient of an organ is an 85 year old, and the oldest recorded donator was 104.

2. Have you made a Living Will?
Where is the paperwork to support this?

A Living Will (also known as Advance Decision) is a written statement (which is not legally binding) which gives you the right to refuse medical treatment under certain circumstances.
A Power of Attorney is a legal document which allows you to choose somebody who you trust to make decisions on your behalf in the future. These might be decisions about your property, your legal affairs or your personal welfare.

3. Have you signed a Power of Attorney? If so, where is the paperwork for this?

It is important that you advise your family and executors if you have registered as an organ donor, completed a Power of Attorney or made a Living Will.

SECTION SEVEN

Where There's a Will...

1. Have you made your Will?

In the UK seven out of ten people die without making a Will, which can create delays and cause significant tax problems.

2. If so, when was it made?

If you have made any amendments to your Will (a codicil), when was the last one made?

4. Is the Will held at your solicitor's office? If so, please supply the name, address and telephone number of your solicitor:

Solicitor's Name: ______________________

Address: ______________________

____

____

Telephone number: ______________________

Email address: ______________________

5. It is strongly recommended that you lodge your Will at a solicitor's office, but if your Will is not there, where is it?

6. For the sake of completeness, who are your executors?
Please supply names, addresses, telephone numbers – home, work and mobile and e-mail addresses of each.

Executor 1's Name: ______________________

Address: ______________________

____

____

Telephone numbers: ______________________

Email address: ______________________

Executor 2's Name: ______________________________

Address: ______________________________

____

____

Telephone numbers: ______________________________

Email address: ______________________________

Executor 3's Name: ______________________________

Address: ______________________________

____

____

Telephone numbers: ______________________________

Email address: ______________________________

Executor 4's Name: ______________________________

Address: ______________________________

____

____

Telephone numbers: ______________________________

Email address: ______________________________

7. Is each executor aware of the location and contents of your Will?
Note: There is no need to inform your executors or any of your beneficiaries about your Will's contents if you do not wish to.

8. Do any of your executors have a copy of this book?

Are they aware that it exists? If not, it would be advisable to mention it.

SECTION EIGHT

Money Matters

One of the most important tasks your executors will have to carry out is to apply for Probate. This consists of identifying and declaring to the Probate Registry Ofiice the value of your estate, that is the sum of your finances and possessions minus your outstanding debts.

Your executors will need to provide proof of your estate's gross value, that is your finances, your possessions and potentially, your home. If you own your home, they will need to provide a valuation certificate from an estate agent, and whilst this is relatively easy to arrange, they may also need to provide valuation certificates for any high-value items you have such as works of art or expensive jewellery. So, you may wish to advise your executors, in the following table, where they can find original purchase receipts or valuations for such items.

It may be useful, and easier, to keep a folder of current policies, pension details, and accounts for referral. This will need to be updated periodically should providers of services change (gas, electric, water, telephone, etc), or if amendments are made to any of the policies or accounts.

If you already have this in place where is the folder or binder?

What colour is it?

As well as providing details of your assets, they will also have to establish what liabilities you have and outstanding monies which you owe, such as loans, mortgage(s), any payment arrears, tax issues etc. The easier you can make it for your executors to gather this information, the sooner Probate can be applied for.

Whilst paperwork surrounding any person's accounts is relatively easy to find within a property, making sense of the myriad of policies, accounts, service providers and invoices, can be more difficult than it would first seem. Outdated bills, statements, and invoices all need to be sieved through and this can be extremely time consuming and complex, particularly if your executors are not familiar with your finances and your property. Even if you have a partner who lives with you, they will, most likely, be too upset to go through such mundane matters as paperwork. Therefore it would be prudent, not to say hugely beneficial, to always keep relevant paperwork in order and easy to find.

Accounts, credit cards, pensions, standing orders and direct debits will all have to be closed and stopped. Your executor may be able to reclaim income tax if you have overpaid tax, so it would be useful to have your Tax Office details available. They will also need to cancel insurance policies to cars, and potentially sell your vehicle so registration documents will be required.

Please supply a list of where your bank accounts are held. For security reasons, do not list the account numbers. Also, mention mortgage lender(s), and all other bodies which should be notified. There is a list of suggested contacts on pages 46 – 48 for reference.

Your executors will also need to find the original documentation for all of the above agreements, policies and accounts.

Where exactly within your property is this original documentation kept?

For the sake of completeness, please list all the property you own. Consider your home, as well as any holiday or investment property you own.

Where are the deeds for each of these properties? *(You may wish to use a blank sheet later in the section if there are a number of properties)*

Note: many people talk about "the deeds" to a property, but most details of property ownership are now held by (and are easily available from) the Land Registry.
If you are unsure about the location of documents which show that you own the property, you can ask the Solicitor who acted for you when you bought it.
Alternatively, if you purchased the property with the help of a mortgage, the lender may know where the relevant documents are.

When completing the list, do not forget to mention subscriptions such as membership fees of clubs and societies from which your estate may be due a refund. (Anything that has the possibility of a refund has * included next to it).

Also, do not forget online accounts, PayPal etc, where there may be funds stored. It may be useful to advise your executors of any alternative names you go under – such as on eBay, or email addresses.

On the next three pages is a list of ideas, some of which may be useful. Complete it if you do not have a file already put together.

FINANCES	DETAILS SUCH AS LOCATION OF PAPERWORK, ETC	ANY USEFUL INFORMATION	DONE ✓
Accountant's Details			
Bank Account (1) Only mention branch			
Bank Account (2) Only mention branch			
Building Society Only mention branch			
Mortgage Provider			
PEPs/ TESSAs			
ISA/Bonds etc			
Premium Bonds			
Hire Purchase Co			
Shares + Broker details			
Endowment Policy			
Pension Provider(s)			
Credit Card (1)			
Credit Card (2)			
Your National Ins No.			
Your Tax Office Ref *			
Any outstanding loan			

FINANCES	DETAILS SUCH AS LOCATION OF PAPERWORK, ETC	ANY USEFUL INFORMATION	DONE ✓
Gas *			
Electricity *			
Water Rates *			
Council Tax *			
Telephone – landline *			
Mobile telephone *			
Internet Provider			
Cable/Satellite TV contract			
Television Rental Co			
TV Licence *			
Store/Loyalty Cards (1)			
Store/Loyalty Cards (2)			
Membership of clubs *			
Ebay user name			
Paypal *			
Email name(s)			
Email name(s)			

FINANCES	DETAILS SUCH AS LOCATION OF PAPERWORK, ETC	ANY USEFUL INFORMATION	DONE ✓
Home Insurance Building *			
Home Insurance Contents *			
Assurance Policy			
Insurance Policy *			
Health Insurance Policy *			
Dental Care Policy			
Travel Insurance Policy *			
Pet Insurance Policy			
Motor Insurance *			
Car Log Book			
Motobility/Parking Card			
Car Warranty details			
Car Rental Agreement*			
Driving Licence			
Passport			
Valuations of High Value Items			

Page intentionally left blank for your notes

Page intentionally left blank for your notes

SECTION NINE

Goods & Chattels

One of the most challenging and potentially stressful aspects of being an executor is the distribution of a deceased's possessions. If there is no surviving spouse or partner, it can be a demanding task to work out what should be left to whom. As second marriages become the norm, live-in partnerships no longer uncommon, and with children from different partners in families, the lines of ownership and the justification of subsequent claims on any single article can become very blurred. Therefore, there can be few more constructive and helpful tasks, no matter how difficult, than pre-determining who should receive what.

Whilst legacies contained within a Will advises of one's wishes in no uncertain terms, the distribution of one's possessions often amply demonstrates an area of uncertainty in all its shades of grey. Without the all-important guidance which could assist them, executors, who are not familiar with the deceased's belongings, may inadvertently give away articles promised to another individual, not knowing of the item's history and relevance. Similarly, antiques and items of great value, which appear to be run of the mill to the untrained eye, may be undersold or worse still, thrown away on the assumption that it is worthless tat.

Whilst some executors will sieve through belongings of the deceased with a fine tooth comb, in order to ensure that all items of monetary and sentimental value are uncovered, others, along with some solicitors, will use house clearance companies to empty a deceased's property as quickly as possible. There is also the chance that some beneficiaries, who are persuasive or forceful, end up with the bulk of the more expensive items, whilst those who may still be grieving are less likely to make their wishes heard and end up with nothing. Sadly, it is often the case of he who shouts loudest gets heard. Such occurrences are far from rare and are the making of family feuds for years to come.

Bereavement is a difficult emotional process where all manner of emotions, such as grief, fear, loss, jealousy, and anger can rage in full flight. If one adds the potential of money and possessions into that mix, there is a powerful cocktail waiting for the smallest spark to ignite it. Anything and everything that can be decided upon in advance will be hugely beneficial to all in the long run.

Items of great value (such as jewellery, works of art etc) can either be bequeathed to specific people in your Will, or sold and form part of the residue of your estate. If, in reading this book, it highlights the need to make changes to your Will, you should talk to your solicitor, or make provision for those alterations immediately. Remaining belongings (referred to as 'chattels') may have personal and sentimental value, and whilst they may not be of great monetary worth, they may have invaluable memories attached to them. Items which have been within the family for generations can be emotionally priceless to some and worthless to others. If you have any such items, it may be worth making a note on one of following blank pages or at the back of this book, detailing the history of the piece in case an executor is unaware of the item's significance. It does not matter how simple or inexpensive the article, the point is its relative sentimental value.

In completing the table on the next page, you also have the opportunity to verify whether you have already promised (either in writing or in conversation) any item to any particular person. Claims made for the ownership of an item after someone's death are legendary, and families frequently fall out over the pettiest of items, so it is in everyone's interest to have this completed.

ITEM DESCRIPTION	WHERE IS IT?	BEQUEATHED TO & CONTACT TEL NO?

1. After death, your family and/or your executors will need to enter your home. Who has access to your property via a spare set of keys? Please list everyone and their contact details as keys will need to be returned to the executors:

Are there any other keys pertaining to your property – such as your back door key, a shed key etc?
Where are these keys?

EXECUTORS:
Choosing when and how to empty a house of belongings is an extremely upsetting issue for many and should be dealt with great sensitivity. Whilst no one would wish a deceased's belongings to remain languishing in a property for years, nor would it be appropriate to empty it with unseeming haste (unless circumstances dictate it to be necessary).
Some religions believe the spirit of the deceased lives on within the property for some days after death, so it may be respectful to bear that in mind if any mourners are spiritually minded.

2. Is your property alarmed? Who knows the code?
It may be useful to supply your executors with the code. For security reasons, do not write it here.

3. Following your passing, there could be mourners who may wish to stay in your property. Please advise whether this is acceptable to you, and does this relate to everyone, or only specific persons. Please specify:

4. Your belongings; who are you expecting to assist in emptying your home of your belongings?

5. Has this been discussed and what, if any, provision has been made to enable this to happen?

6. What do you wish the executors to do with your clothes?

7. What do you wish the executors to do with your furniture?

8. Are the beneficiaries aware that you are leaving these items to them?

9. Is there anyone who you would prefer not to enter your home after your passing?

10. Do you have a safe in your home?
If so, who is aware of its location and its code?
For security reasons, it is advisable to pass this information on to your executors rather than writing it down here.

11. Similarly, are there any items kept for safekeeping with your bank or elsewhere? If so, what items and who is keeping them?
Is there any documentation to support this and where is it?

12. Are there any items of any description within your home which belong to someone else? If so, what items and to whom do they belong?
Where can they be found?

13. Does anyone owe you any money? Is there any proof of this?

Do you wish your executors to try to recover this money and add it to your estate?

14. Do you owe anyone any money, other than outstanding bills, which will be paid out of your estate? Is there any proof of this?

15. If you have any assets, such as your home, or any items of high value which will need to be sold, do you have any preference as to which agent is used to sell those assets? Please supply any names and contact numbers:

16. If you own your own home, are there any guarantees which may be needed when selling the property? (For example, for the boiler, the GCH, DPC, Double Glazing, Conservatory, Extensions etc.)
Where can such guarantees be found?

17. Does your property have a loft, cellar, or cupboard which is not obvious to your executors? Is it empty or are belongings stored there?

Page intentionally left blank for your notes

SECTION TEN

Children

Adequate provision should be made for children under the age of 18. With today's complicated lifestyles and life choices, this is clearly beyond the scope of this book. It must be dealt with in your Will, with the benefit of guidance from a competent solicitor, who may recommend trusts and should offer suitable advice.

Particular attention should be given, and caution exercised, if you have a vulnerable child who may need specialist care into adulthood. In such cases, it is crucial that advice is sought from a solicitor who is fully conversant in not just the various trusts which are available, but also has an appreciation and experience as to the level of care your child may need. MENCAP have seen many cases where badly drafted Wills have had dire consequences for the child. If a suitable trust is not set up, a beneficiary can end up inheriting large sums of money which they may not have the capacity to deal with and which may, in turn, make them vulnerable to abuse from others. There is also the risk that a poorly considered legacy may affect their eligibility to means-tested benefits. MENCAP provides a range of guidance literature and free telephone advice to parents and carers of anyone with a learning disability. The organisation also holds a list of recommended solicitors who are fully conversant with both the financial and practical needs of the vulnerable. For further information visit www.mencap.org.uk/willsandtrusts.

If you have children under the age of 18, your solicitor will, most likely, advise you to appoint guardians for your children for worst case scenarios. Once guardians have been selected and agreed upon, you may wish to leave instructions of some kind regarding education, religious upbringing, residence etc. These will need to be reviewed from time to time, as your children mature and their circumstances change.

For the sake of completeness, it is worth clarifying a few details.
Please write the names of your children and their dates of birth:

1. Please give the names of your children's guardians and their contact details:

Guardian 1's Name: ______________________________

Address: ______________________________

____

____

____

Telephone numbers: ______________________________

Email address: ______________________________

Guardian 2's Name: ______________________________

Address: ______________________________

____

____

____

Telephone numbers: ______________________________

Email address: ______________________________

What relation are the guardians to the children (if any)?

2. Have you left any written instructions for the guardians of your children as to your preferences in any of the topics raised earlier in this section? (education/religion etc). If so, where are these instructions?

3. If your children are still living at home, please say where Birth Certificates are kept:

4. Are there any special requests with regard to your children *which have not been mentioned* in your Will which you wish to address now?
Use overleaf if necessary.

Page intentionally left blank for your notes

Page intentionally left blank for your notes

SECTION ELEVEN

Pooch, Puss and Pets

If you have a pet, someone will need to take care of him/her. Whilst anyone close may know the pet's name, few will know about the day-to-day care that your pet is used to, so completing this section will be very helpful. If you have more than one pet, perhaps complete the answers below in different coloured pens for each animal. Alternatively, it may be useful to have a folder specifically relating to your pet(s).

1. What is your pet's name, breed and date of birth?

2. If your pet is a pedigree, do you have the documentation to support this? You may wish to include details of the breeder.

3. Is there anyone in particular you would like to look after him/her?

4. Equally important, is there anyone who you would rather did not take care of your pet?

5. Are there any special instructions which are needed for the care of the pet?

6. What type of food does your pet eat? Does your pet have any special dietary needs?

7. Does your pet have any vaccination certificates? Where are they?

8. Does your pet have any medical conditions?

9. Does your pet attend a particular veterinary practice?
Please supply details of the name and address of the vet:

10. Is your pet covered by any form of insurance (for example, in respect of vet's fees?) The documentation should be left with other policies in your file.

11. Which kennel/cattery does your pet normally go to?

12. Is your pet micro-chipped? Where is the documentation to support this?

13. If you have assembled a file on your pet, where is the file, and what colour is it?

SECTION TWELVE

Last Orders

Whilst your Will serves the role of bequeathing your assets, it does not cater for core issues which have to be addressed on a more personal level. Having completed this book, you have given the executors of your Will the opportunity to do their utmost to ensure that your wishes are carried out to the letter. Please note, however, that this is a Letter of Wishes, NOT a legally binding document and the wishes laid out in this booklet are advisory, and not mandatory.

If there are any last requests which involve your estate, you should ask your solicitor whether you need to alter your Will.

Are there any issues which concern you which have not been covered in these pages?

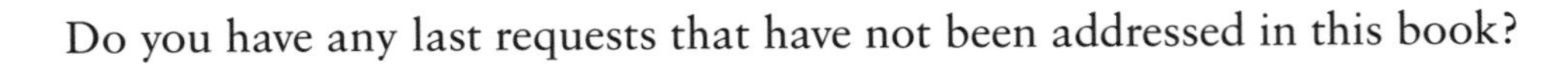

Do you have any last requests that have not been addressed in this book?

In completing *Last Orders* you have had to think about some difficult issues. In providing your executors and those you leave behind with this information, you have contributed to making your passing, and the arrangements which ensue, as clear-cut as is possible. Whilst the questions may have appeared to be unfeeling and depressing, you have advised your executors of your last wishes, and generously helped them at a time when they are likely to be grieving.

Once you have completed this book, it would be advisable to sign and date the next page to verify that the content represents your wishes. It is important that this is not witnessed, as this could invalidate your Will. Equally, it is advisable not to leave stray notes which are neither included in your Will nor a codicil, as it could cause significant ill feeling when they are discovered to be legally invalid.

Finally, having thoughtfully taken the time and made the effort to complete this book, it is essential that it can be found by your executors or anyone arranging your funeral. Therefore it would be useful to discuss any or all of the contents with them. Alternatively, you may wish to tell them where to find this book when the time comes.

There are a number of blank pages following this page for any special thoughts you wish to share with your loved ones.

Signed ____

Dated ____

Notes

Notes

Notes

Notes

Notes

Notes

To order further copies of LAST ORDERS please send a copy of the coupon to:

STELLAR BOOKS
DUNHAM GATEHOUSE
CHARCOAL ROAD
BOWDON
CHESHIRE
WA14 4RY

Alternatively you may order further copies direct from the website www.lastorders.org

Please send me _____ copies of: LAST ORDERS at £12.99 each

P&P within the UK is Free of Charge

I enclose a UK sterling cheque or postal order payable to Stellar Books for £ __________

NAME: ______________________________

ADDRESS: ______________________________

____

____

POSTCODE: ______________________________